INTROI

This workbook is intended as a study aid for those who use *A Catholic Guide to the Bible*. It is made up of multiple-choice and true/false questions and can help you develop a clearer understanding of the Bible in an enjoyable and challenging way. It is designed to provide both education and entertainment, as crossword puzzles and word games do.

A general rule for true/false questions: If part of a statement is true and part is false, the statement should be marked false. A general rule for multiple-choice questions: If it appears that more than one choice may be correct, select the choice which fits best according to the text.

We suggest that you read a chapter of the textbook and the Bible passages listed in that chapter. Then answer the questions in the test. This will allow you to evaluate your understanding of what you have studied. After answering the questions, you can check your responses by going back to the textbook and Bible. Then study in more detail those areas you are unsure about or have answered incorrectly. Make corrections where necessary.

This workbook may be used by groups. Participants, after reading the text and answering the questions, can compare responses as a starting point for discussion. The questions are designed to highlight important material and to encourage study and discussion.

This workbook may serve as an outline for classes taught by an instructor. After students read a chapter of the text and answer the questions, the instructor can go through the questions in order, asking the students for their answers. This will provide a framework for explaining difficult material and for encouraging class participation and discussion.

Groups and classes may also wish to review the Questions for Discussion and Reflection and the Activities at the end of each chapter of the textbook.

A recommendation: Begin and end each chapter with a prayer to the Holy Spirit for guidance and understanding.

God bless you!

Father Oscar Lukefahr, C.M.

CHAPTER ONE
Bibles, Beliefs, and Beginnings

1. T F The Bible is interpreted in different ways by Christians, and the problems involved in interpreting the Bible are increased by the complexities of language and cultural differences.

2. T F The Bible was written over a span of ten thousand years.

3. T F God is the author of the Bible in the sense that God dictated words to the human authors, who then recorded what God spoke to them.

4. T F The Catholic Church teaches that God spoke "through" the human authors of the Bible, allowing them to use their own talents, abilities, and styles of writing.

5. T F Study and interpretation of the Bible are often necessary if we want to gain a proper understanding of its meaning.

6. T F Because the Bible is the word of God, it is not right for Catholics to change their understanding of biblical passages.

7. ___ Recent archaeological finds have helped scholars make great progress in their understanding of the Bible; an important discovery in 1947 was that of (a) original Bible manuscripts; (b) the Gutenberg Bible; (c) the Dead Sea Scrolls; (d) medieval copies of the Bible.

8. T F Because of recent archaeological discoveries, we are perhaps in a better position to understand the original meaning of the biblical authors than anyone since the time of Christ.

9. T F Because the Bible is the word of God, it cannot contain fictional stories or fables.

10. T F Aided by scholarly research, average people can learn to recognize and understand the literary forms of the Bible.

11. T F There is more agreement today among Protestant and Catholic Scripture scholars about the substance of the original biblical texts than there was in years past.

12. ___ There are many ways to translate the Bible. English versions which produce a more readable text by freely translating and restating ideas are called (a) literal translations; (b) manuscripts; (c) analogies; (d) paraphrases.

13. ___ The Catholic English version most commonly used in liturgical worship in the United States is (a) *The New American Bible;* (b) *The Jerusalem Bible;* (c) *New International Bible;* (d) *The Living Bible.*

14. T F Those who are beginning to read the Bible should realize that it is a collection of many books.

15. T F The major divisions of the Bible are called the Old Testament and the New Testament, and the entire Old Testament was written before the time of Christ.

16. T F In the system commonly used to locate verses in the Bible, 1 Pt 2:10 is a citation referring the reader to the Letter of Peter, Chapter 1, Verses two to ten.

17. T F 1 Kgs 2:1-4, 10-11 refers to the First Book of Kings, Chapter 2, Verses 1 to 4 and 10 to 11.

18. ___ There are many Bible study aids available: one which lists each occurrence of every word in the Bible and gives the place where each word may be found is a (a) commentary; (b) Bible atlas; (c) concordance; (d) dictionary.

19. T F The main reason why the Bible is a bestseller is that it is inspired by God.

20. T F The best way to approach the Bible is to see it as great literature to be investigated in the same way as other "great books" are studied.

21. T F The Bible has been given to us by God to help us answer the great questions in life.

22. T F The Bible should be seen as a means for dialogue with the living God.

23. T F Our goal in studying the Bible should be to learn what God says in the Bible *and* to believe what God says *and* to act upon it.

24. ___ When we open our Bible, we may correctly have as our purpose (a) study; (b) prayer; (c) guidance; (d) a, b, or c.

25. T F Whatever our purpose in turning to the Bible, we should always begin with prayer.

CHAPTER TWO

Authors of the Bible: God and People

1. T F   Our Jewish-Christian tradition teaches us that God speaks to us through nature, events, people, and prayer.

2. T F   We listen to God by "tuning" our senses, intellect, memory, will, imagination, and emotions to the reality of God's presence, action, and communication.

3. T F   Sin and excessive concentration on earthly pursuits can make it difficult for us to direct our attention to God.

4. T F   We can be sure that biblical authors were aware of the fact that they were being inspired by God.

5. T F   The perceptions of God preserved in the Bible differ from non-biblical perceptions because those in the Bible are recognized by the Church community as inspired by God.

6. T F   The Bible is relevant for us today because it can give us the authentic visions of God received from Abraham, Moses, Luke, Paul, and the Christian community.

7. ___   The first biblical personality to live in Palestine (Canaan) was (a) Abraham; (b) Jacob; (c) Moses; (d) David.

8. T F   Isaac and his twelve sons migrated from Palestine to Egypt, where the Hebrews became slaves.

9. T F   Moses led the Hebrews from slavery in Egypt, but he did not lead them into the Promised Land.

10. ___   The first king of Israel was (a) Joshua; (b) Saul; (c) David; (d) Abram.

11. ___ The king who made Israel a Middle East power was (a) Saul; (b) Goliath; (c) David; (d) Solomon.

12. T F Solomon built a great Temple in Jerusalem but alienated the people, setting the stage for civil war under his son Rehoboam in 922 B.C.

13. T F In the divided kingdoms, the capital of Judah was Samaria, and the capital of Israel was Jerusalem.

14. T F The northern kingdom of Israel was defeated by Assyria in 721; the southern kingdom of Judah was conquered by Babylon in 587.

15. T F When Cyrus the Persian defeated Babylon, he allowed the Jewish exiles to return home in 539. Within 25 years, they had rebuilt the Temple and the city walls.

16. ___ In 167 the Maccabee family led the Jewish people in revolt against (a) Alexander the Great; (b) Egypt; (c) Syria; (d) Assyria.

17. T F Jesus was born during the reign of Herod the Great.

18. T F Jesus' message that God's kingdom had come in him was opposed by the Pharisees and Herodians but accepted by the Sadducees and a majority of the people.

19. T F Jesus was crucified on a Friday. After he rose from the dead, he appeared often to his apostles and to others.

20. ___ The Pharisee who led a persecution against Jesus' followers was (a) Stephen; (b) Saul; (c) Pilate; (d) Herod the Great.

21. T F In spite of persecutions, Christianity flourished during the first centuries after Christ's Resurrection.

22. ___ The Roman Emperor Constantine issued the edict of Milan, granting religious tolerance to Christians, in A.D. (a) 41; (b) 100; (c) 313; (d) 393.

23. T F Those parts of the Bible dealing with Abraham and Moses were probably written during their lifetimes.

24. ___ The document which codified laws of north and south into the Pentateuch was the (a) Yahwist; (b) Elohist; (c) Deuteronomist; (d) Priestly.

25. ___ The spiritual leaders who urged the people to be faithful to God's covenant after 1000 B.C. were the (a) judges; (b) kings; (c) Samaritans; (d) prophets.

26. ___ The "persecution" literature which used visions, codes, and symbols was (a) proverbs; (b) apocalypse; (c) psalms; (d) apocrypha.

27. T F The Old Testament does not teach that the soul is immortal.

28. ___ The Hebrew version of the Old Testament was called the (a) Septuagint; (b) Alexandrian; (c) Douay; (d) Palestinian.

29. T F The Greek collection of Old Testament books was not finalized until Christians decided upon their Bible, but the Hebrew collection was finalized before the birth of Christ.

30. T F The first written work of the New Testament, the Gospel of Mark, was composed in about A.D. 51.

31. T F All the books of the Old Testament were written before Christ, and all books of the New Testament were written by about A.D. 125.

32. T F Church councils accepted the 46 books of the Septuagint and 27 books of the New Testament as inspired by God.

33. T F Protestant Bibles have seven more books in the Old Testament than do Catholic Bibles.

34. ___ The languages used in the Bible were Hebrew, Greek, and (a) Syrian; (b) Aramaic; (c) Egyptian; (d) Latin.

35. T F Thanks to cooperation among Scripture scholars, modern English translations of the Bible are in substantial agreement, and accurately relay to us the ideas and feelings conveyed in the original languages.

CHAPTER THREE

Reading and Interpreting the Bible

1. T F The reevaluation of biblical books based on recent archaeological discoveries has enhanced our ability to understand the real meaning of the Bible.

2. T F This reevaluation has shown that some Bible books formerly thought to be historical are really not, and it has shown that the essential historical foundation of our Christian faith is uncertain.

3. ____ Interpreting the Bible by attempting to go back to the original intent of its authors, analyzing their times, culture, language and circumstances, is a method called the (a) fundamentalist; (b) literary; (c) unhistorical; (d) contextual.

4. T F It is possible to interpret and understand the meaning of any part of the Bible by examining the words alone.

5. ____ Catholic principles for interpreting the Bible include all the following except: (a) the contextual approach; (b) seeing a passage in the light of other passages; (c) recognizing the special qualities of Aramaic; (d) emphasizing the personal and subjective nature of interpretation.

6. ____ Catholic principles for interpreting the Bible include all the following except: (a) realizing that the Bible often emphasizes only one side of an issue at a time; (b) seeing the Old Testament in the light of the New; (c) stating that the Bible cannot report erroneous attitudes; (d) using objective principles spelled out by scholars and endorsed by the Church; (e) c and d.

7. ___ When the Old Testament reports that God told Hebrew leaders to slaughter their enemies, it is most likely that (a) this actually happened; (b) the leaders were mistaken in thinking that God wanted this; (c) God wants evil people to be eliminated; (d) this was the attitude of Jesus Christ.

8. ___ Inspiration means that (a) God is the author of the Bible; (b) there can be no error in the Bible; (c) the human authors of the Bible were infallible; (d) a, b, and c.

9. T F Since God is author of the Bible, what God wants to convey through the words of the Bible is infallibly true.

10. ___ Truth can be expressed in (a) history; (b) poetry; (c) fables; (d) a, b, and c; (e) a and b only.

11. T F Something can be true without being historical.

12. T F Fictional stories can teach important religious truths.

13. T F Since the human authors of the Bible were inspired by God, they could not make mistakes in their writings.

14. T F The Bible should give us certainty about every issue, and there can be no contradictions in the Bible.

15. T F The Bible came from the Church, not the Church from the Bible.

16. T F In choosing certain works for the Bible as inspired by God, the Catholic Church formed our present-day list of 73 books and expressed the truths which form the basis of our belief.

17. ___ "Tradition," as understood by the Catholic Church, includes (a) interpretation of the Bible; (b) decisions of councils; (c) creeds; (d) worship; (e) a, b, c, and d.

18. T F Doctrines of the Catholic Church need not be explicitly declared in the Bible.

19. T F Divine revelation is made up of the Bible and sacred tradition.

20. T F The Catholic Church teaches that all doctrine must be in harmony with the Bible.

21. T F The Bible should be the only source of our beliefs.

22. T F The original Christian Bible was formed in communities of believers presided over by Catholic bishops and finalized into a collection through the decisions of councils of Catholic bishops.

23. T F From the first through the fifteenth centuries, manuscripts of the Bible were copied by hand by Protestants and Catholics.
24. T F The reading of the Bible at Catholic celebrations of the Eucharist is a relatively new development.
25. T F The Catholic Church encourages its members to read the Bible.
26. T F Ignorance of the Scriptures is ignorance of Christ.
27. T F When we pick up the Bible, God speaks to us through the same words addressed to Abraham and Moses, and Jesus speaks to us as he did to the apostles.
28. T F Because the Bible is inspired by God, its words will always have the same meaning for us.
29. T F When we read the Bible, God is aware of what we are doing.
30. T F God speaks to us in the Bible, and we reply through our prayer and our life choices.

CHAPTER FOUR

First Steps in the Old Testament: Adam to Moses

1. T F Catholics can find their "spiritual roots" in the Old Testament.
2. ___ The Pentateuch was completed about (a) the time of Moses; (b) 1000 B.C.; (c) 550 B.C.; (d) 50 B.C.
3. T F The relevance of the Pentateuch comes from the fact that it records our family past and, under divine inspiration, answers the most basic questions in life.
4. ___ Of the four traditions which are the main sources of the Pentateuch, the one from which the first story of creation was taken is (a) Yahwist; (b) Elohist; (c) Deuteronomist; (d) Priestly.
5. T F In the poetic structure of Genesis 1, there is an interlocking of days to make memorization easier: day one is connected to day six, day two to day five, and day three to day four.
6. T F The concept that human beings are made in God's image may reflect our call to be representatives of God in caring for the world God has given us.
7. T F Genesis teaches the "how" of creation, while science teaches the "why" of creation.
8. T F Human beings are created after animals in the first story of creation but before animals in the second.

9. T F The first story of creation deals with the problem of suffering, while the second teaches us to rest from work one day out of the week.

10. T F The main purpose of Genesis 1–3 is not to give an historical account of the first people on earth but to teach basic religious truths about God and ourselves.

11. T F In Genesis 12–25, the names Abram and Abraham refer to the same man, Sarai and Sarah to the same woman.

12. ___ When Abraham migrated from Haran to Canaan, he did *not* take (a) Sarah; (b) Lot; (c) Isaac; (d) their possessions (Gn 12:1-9).

13. T F In Genesis 15, God promises that Abraham will have descendants and that they will be given a land to dwell in.

14. ___ Abraham's children were named Isaac and (a) Hagar; (b) Ishmael; (c) Esau; (d) Jacob (Gn 15:1–17:27).

15. ___ The sign of the covenant God made with Abraham was (a) the Ten Commandments; (b) baptism; (c) circumcision; (d) human sacrifice (Gn 15:1–17:27).

16. T F Among the Israelites, Abraham was renowned for his faith.

17. T F Even though Jacob deceived his father, God was able to use Jacob's misdeed to accomplish divine purposes.

18. T F The mother of Jacob was Rebekah, and one of his wives was named Rachel (Gn 25:19-26; 29:28).

19. T F Jacob and Esau remained mortal enemies until death (Gn 33).

20. ___ Israel was another name for (a) Abram; (b) Isaac; (c) Esau; (d) Jacob (Gn 35).

21. ___ When Joseph, the son of Jacob, was reunited with his eleven brothers, he bestowed special gifts on (a) Reuben; (b) Judah; (c) Levi; (d) Benjamin (Gn 45).

22. ___ Between Joseph and Moses, there was a passage of years numbering about (a) 100; (b) 500; (c) 1000; (d) 2000.

23. T F The plagues which allowed the Hebrews to escape from Egypt are probably described in the Bible as they occurred in history.

24. ___ The literary form of the Exodus is best described as (a) epic; (b) fable; (c) history; (d) fiction.

25. T F The Exodus has no basis in history.

26. ___ Exodus 1 describes the fate of Hebrew slaves as including all these except: (a) fieldwork; (b) building cities; (c) rowing Egyptian warships; (d) making bricks.

27. ___ Exodus 14 shows God's protection for the Hebrews in all the following signs except: (a) Pharaoh's capture; (b) an angel; (c) a fiery cloud; (d) a strong east wind.

28. T F All the laws found in the Book of Exodus were written before the death of Moses.

29. T F Among the most important religious lessons to be learned from Exodus are that God wants to be close to us and wants us to be truly free.

30. T F After God gave the commandments to Moses, the people requested that God speak directly to them (Ex 20).

31. T F When Moses sprinkled blood on the Israelites at Mount Sinai, he was symbolizing their sinfulness.

32. ___ The leader in the making of the golden calf was (a) Joshua; (b) Aaron; (c) Moses; (d) Levi (Ex 32).

33. ___ The altar described in Exodus 38 was plated with (a) gold; (b) silver; (c) bronze; (d) iron.

34. T F The central theme of the Book of Leviticus is stated as "Be holy, for I, the LORD, your God, am holy."

35. T F Leviticus bids us to love our neighbor as ourself.

36. ___ The Jewish feast at which the people were to gather tree branches was (a) Passover; (b) Pentecost; (c) Atonement; (d) Booths (Lv 23).

37. T F Numbers was meant to help Israelites see themselves as a holy community, organized by the will of God.

38. T F Moses' sister Miriam died at Kadesh; his brother Aaron and Aaron's son Eleazar died at Mount Hor (Nm 20).

39. T F According to Numbers 20, Moses' faithfulness in bringing water from the rock was pleasing to God.

40. ___ In the story of the talking donkey (Nm 22), an angel tells Balaam that if his donkey had not stopped, the angel would have killed (a) Balaam; (b) the donkey; (c) both; (d) neither.

41. T F It is likely that the story of the talking donkey is a fable meant to teach religious truth.

42. T F Deuteronomy means "second law" or "copy of the law."

43. T F According to Deuteronomy, Moses saw the Promised Land but did not enter it.

44. T F The Book of Deuteronomy in its present form was almost certainly written by Moses.

45. T F The Book of Deuteronomy was composed for the Israelites who survived the Babylonian Exile.

46. T F The Deuteronomist tradition is not found elsewhere in the Pentateuch or in other books of the Bible.

47. T F Because Deuteronomy is inspired by God, its theology cannot be less developed than the theology of the New Testament.

48. T F According to Deuteronomy 1, Moses addressed his sermon to the people during their fortieth year in the desert.

49. T F The Ten Commandments are found in the Books of Exodus and Deuteronomy; the great commandment to love God with all our heart is found in Deuteronomy (Dt 6).

50. T F The Pentateuch is a unit made of five books which may be said to form the "constitution" of the Jewish people.

CHAPTER FIVE

The Historical Books: Joshua to the Exile

1. T F Judaism and Christianity originated from real historical events.
2. T F Taken as a whole, history in the Bible is not history in the modern sense of the word.
3. ___ The primary purpose of biblical history is to focus on (a) the sequence of events; (b) relationships between God and people; (c) major events; (d) dates and places.
4. ___ Readers should *least* expect to find in the Bible's historical books (a) broad religious themes; (b) specific moral directives; (c) events and personalities; (d) a framework for the better understanding of sacred Scripture.
5. ___ The Deuteronomist history includes all the following except: (a) Judges; (b) 1 and 2 Kings; (c) Exodus; (d) Joshua; (e) 1 and 2 Samuel.
6. ___ The Deuteronomist history was edited into its present form about (a) 721; (b) 620; (c) 550; (d) 400.
7. T F The Deuteronomist history was inspired by God, but there are weaknesses and limitations in its theology.
8. T F The details of the conquest of Palestine, as described in the Book of Joshua, can be verified from the Book of Judges and from other historical records.
9. T F Because the Bible clearly states that God commanded the Jews to massacre their enemies, we can be sure that God actually did so.

10. ___ When the Israelites went into the Promised Land, the first to enter the Jordan River was (a) the Ark; (b) Joshua; (c) Moses; (d) the army (Jos 3).

11. ___ The main lesson of Joshua 6 is (a) enemies should be eliminated; (b) trumpets weaken walls; (c) obedience to God is rewarded; (d) seven is a magic number.

12. ___ Joshua's speech before his death did *not* mention (a) the Exodus; (b) Moses' death; (c) crossing the Jordan; (d) the covenant (Jos 24).

13. ___ The Judges were (a) legal experts; (b) elected officials; (c) kings; (d) heroes and heroines.

14. ___ A lesson *not* found in Judges is that (a) disobedience brings misfortune; (b) obedience wins God's favor; (c) humanity needs salvation; (d) the time of the Judges was the high point of Israel's history.

15. T F The story of Samson relates his loss of strength to the fact that he allowed a pagan woman to undermine his consecration to God (Jgs 15–16).

16. T F The literary form and content of Ruth are similar to that of Judges.

17. ___ Ruth said the words "Wherever you go, I will go" to (a) her future husband; (b) her mother-in-law; (c) Boaz; (d) God (Ru 1–4).

18. ___ Ruth 4 does *not* mention that Ruth was related to (a) Moses; (b) Boaz; (c) Jesse; (d) David.

19. T F The First and Second Books of Samuel originate from a number of sources.

20. T F The First and Second Books of Samuel are classified by scholars as salvation history and, therefore, contain little reliable historical data.

21. ___ Samuel was a (a) general; (b) prophet; (c) king; (d) inspired author of the books named after him; (e) b and d.

22. ___ Saul's anointing by Samuel was witnessed by (a) no one; (b) Saul's servant; (c) Saul's family; (d) thirty guests (1 Sm 9:1–10:1).

23. ___ David, in confronting Goliath, spoke words that showed his belief that victory would come from (a) his sword; (b) his sling; (c) God; (d) Israel's army (1 Sm 17).

24. ___ Saul died in battle with (a) Egypt; (b) David's men; (c) Jabesh-Gilead; (d) the Philistines (1 Sm 31).

25. T F David became king first of the northern tribes of Israel, then of the southern tribe of Judah.

26. T F David conquered Jerusalem and brought the Ark there, thus making Jerusalem the political and religious center of his kingdom.

27. T F David committed adultery with Tamar and then murdered her husband, Uriah.

28. T F Nathan's promise of an everlasting kingdom for David gave later generations hope for a messiah who would come from David's family and restore Israel's fortunes.

29. ___ David reigned as king for (a) 40 years; (b) 20 years; (c) 50 years; (d) 10 years (2 Sm 5).

30. ___ When Nathan accused David of sin, he told a story about a (a) lion; (b) soldier; (c) lamb; (d) donkey (2 Sm 11:1–12:15).

31. ___ In the battle which ended Absolom's rebellion against David, Absolom was slain by (a) Abner; (b) Joab; (c) David; (d) Jonathan (2 Sm 18:1-17).

32. T F Shortly before his death, David killed his brother Adonijah, then appointed Solomon as king.

33. T F Solomon was noted for his wisdom, and he remained faithful to the Lord all his life.

34. T F The northern tribes rebelled against Solomon's son, Rehoboam, and appointed Jeroboam as their king.

35. T F The kings of the north were generally faithful and effective leaders, while those of the south were not.

36. T F The stories about the prophets in 1 and 2 Kings contain legends and fables intended to teach religious messages.

37. ___ In making a difficult decision, Solomon showed his wisdom when he called for a (a) pen; (b) scale; (c) jury; (d) sword (1 Kgs 3).

38. T F Hadad, Rezon, and Jeroboam were allies and friends of Solomon (1 Kgs 11).

39. ___ After the revolt of the northern tribes, their king decided to win their religious loyalty by making (a) an ark; (b) golden calves; (c) a covenant with God; (d) a new Torah (1 Kgs 12).

40. ___ The wife of King Ahab was (a) Delilah; (b) Bathsheba; (c) Jezebel; (d) Naboth (1 Kgs 21).

41. T F Samaria, the capital of Israel, was destroyed by the Assyrians in 721, and almost 30 thousand Israelites were forced into exile.

42. T F Assyria laid siege to Jerusalem in 701 but did not conquer it; less than 100 years later, Assyria was conquered by Babylon.

43. ___ A king of Judah who worshiped pagan gods was (a) Azariah (Uzziah); (b) Hezekiah; (c) Amon; (d) Josiah.

44. T F Babylon defeated Assyria, took control of Jerusalem in 597, conquered and burned it in 587, and deported thousands of Jews to Babylonia.

45. T F From 600 to 550, the population of Judah dropped from about 250 thousand to less than 50 thousand.

46. T F The Jewish exiles were treated harshly in Babylon and had to abandon the faith of their ancestors.

47. T F According to 2 Kings 2, Elisha saw Elijah being taken up to heaven.

48. T F The story about Elisha, the boys, and the bears almost certainly happened just as it is described in 2 Kings 2.

49. ___ In 2 Kings 17, the Deuteronomist gives as reasons for the fall of Israel all the following except: (a) worship of false gods; (b) disregarding the commandments; (c) imitating the Philistines; (d) fortunetelling and divination.

50. T F The Books of Samuel and Kings show us that disobedience to God, abuse of power, and lust can destroy us.

CHAPTER SIX

The Historical Books:
The Postexilic Period

1. T F Cyrus, king of Persia, defeated Babylonia in 539 and in 538 allowed the Jewish exiles to return home.

2. ___ The prince who led the first band of exiles back to Jerusalem was (a) Nehemiah; (b) Zerubbabel; (c) Ezra; (d) Sheshbazzar.

3. T F It seems likely that most of the Jews who left Babylon for Jerusalem had actually been exiled from Jerusalem by Nebuchadnezzar.

4. ___ The man who led the Jews in rebuilding the Temple in 515 was (a) Nehemiah; (b) Zerubbabel; (c) Ezra; (d) Sheshbazzar.

5. ___ The official who saw to the rebuilding of Jerusalem's walls in 445 was (a) Nehemiah; (b) Zerubbabel; (c) Ezra; (d) Sheshbazzar.

6. ___ The priest who instructed the people in the Law was (a) Nehemiah; (b) Zerubbabel; (c) Ezra; (d) Sheshbazzar.

7. ___ The Chronicler's history has all the following purposes except: (a) spotlighting the Jerusalem Temple; (b) correcting the Deuteronomist notion that good is rewarded and sin punished; (c) idealizing past heroes; (d) emphasizing God's greatness.

8. T F As a general rule, the Chronicler tends to emphasize the sins of David and Solomon, while the Deuteronomist tends to gloss over their failings.

9. ___ In 1 Chronicles 12 and 2 Chronicles 14 we see evidence of the Chronicler's use of all these literary devices except: (a) lists of names; (b) inflated numbers; (c) exact dates; (d) idealized salvation history.

10. T F The Books of Ezra and Nehemiah, like 1 and 2 Chronicles, are best described as "idealized salvation history."

11. T F Both Ezra and Nehemiah encouraged the Jews to intermarry with foreigners as a way of winning converts to Judaism.

12. ___ In the first return to Jerusalem, the Jews brought with them all the following except: (a) gold and silver; (b) cattle; (c) the Ark; (d) temple utensils (Ezr 1).

13. ___ The prophets who encouraged the rebuilding of the Temple were (a) Haggai and Zechariah; (b) Elijah and Elisha; (c) Isaiah and Jeremiah; (d) Amos and Hosea (Ezr 6).

14. T F It is clear from Nehemiah 4 that while there was political opposition to rebuilding Jerusalem's walls, there was no real danger of a military attack.

15. ___ After Ezra read the Law to the people of Jerusalem, he said that they should (a) repent; (b) rejoice; (c) confess their sins; (d) attack their enemies (Neh 8).

16. T F From the Chronicler, we can learn reverence for God, love for ancestors, enthusiasm for obedience, and the desire to worship God properly.

17. T F Less than 70 years passed from the mission of Ezra to the time of Alexander the Great.

18. T F Alexander the Great ruled over territory from Greece to India but did not attack Jerusalem or Samaria.

19. T F For more than a century after Alexander's death, Palestine was fought over by successors of Ptolemy of Egypt, called Ptolemies, and successors of Seleucus Nicator, known as Seleucids.

20. ___ The effort after Alexander to impose Greek traditions on other cultures was called (a) Ptolemism; (b) Seleucidism; (c) Hellenism; (d) Antiochism.

21. ___ In the Maccabean revolt against the Syrian persecution of 167, Jewish forces were led by four members of the Maccabee family. The correct sequence of their leadership was (a) Simon, Judas, Jonathan, Mattathias; (b) M, Jo, Ju, S; (c) Ju, Jo, S, M; (d) M, Ju, Jo, S.

22. ___ Jews celebrate Judas Maccabeus' rededication of the Jerusalem Temple in 164 B.C. at the Feast of (a) Purim; (b) Yom Kippur; (c) Hanukkah; (d) Sukkoth; (e) Pesach.

23. ___ The dynasty formed when the Jews won back their independence in 142 is known as the (a) Hasidean; (b) Hasmonean; (c) Sadducean; (d) Judean.

24. T F Beginning in 90, the Pharisees waged civil war against the high priest, Alexander Janneus, and his allies, the aristocratic Sadducees.

25. T F In the first century B.C., Judea expanded its borders almost to the limits of David's kingdom but then became a vassal state of Rome in 63.

26. ___ Herod the Great, who began his rule over Judea in 37, would *not* have been called "Great" because of his (a) construction programs; (b) governmental organization; (c) benevolent reign; (d) rebuilding the Temple.

27. T F The Books of Tobit, Judith, and Esther can best be classified not as history but as religious historical novels.

28. T F While the stories of Tobit, Judith, and Esther are set in Assyria, Babylon, and Persia, these books were actually written for Jews who lived after these empires had fallen.

29. T F Tobit, Judith, and Esther provide us with accurate dates for key events and important people in history.

30. ___ The Book of Tobit exemplifies all these virtues except: (a) devotion to temple worship; (b) reverence for God; (c) love of family; (d) openness to foreigners.

31. ___ In Tobit 4, Tobit sends his son to Media to obtain (a) money; (b) a wife; (c) a job; (d) a and b.

32. T F The Book of Judith was written to give hope to the Jews who were exiled in Babylon.

33. ___ Judith promised Uzziah that (a) God would send rain; (b) God would rescue Israel; (c) she would reveal her plan before leaving Bethulia; (d) nothing (Jdt 8).

34. ___ The story of Esther is set in (a) Babylon; (b) Media; (c) Persia; (d) Judea.

35. ___ The Book of Esther relates to the Feast of (a) Purim; (b) Yom Kippur; (c) Hanukkah; (d) Sukkoth; (e) Pesach.

36. T F We may see in the Book of Esther a foreshadowing of Christ's victory over Satan, even though the author did not intend this.

37. T F Mordecai, enemy of the Jews, was hanged on a gibbet he had prepared for Haman (Est 9).

38. ___ According to Esther 9, Jews were to celebrate their victory over their enemies by all of the following except: (a) feasting; (b) gifts to the poor; (c) sending gifts of food; (d) fasting.

39. ___ The title for 1 and 2 Maccabees comes from the name given to the leader of the Jewish anti-Seleucid guerrilla forces, Judas Maccabeus. Maccabeus means (a) sword; (b) hammer; (c) shield; (d) victory.

40. ___ Study the following statements:
1) The First and Second Books of Maccabees were written in Hebrew by the same author about 100 B.C.
2) The Second Book of Maccabees is more reliable in giving historical details than is 1 Maccabees.
Of these statements: (a) both are true; (b) both are false; (c) 1 is false, 2 is true; (d) 1 is true, 2 is false.

41. T F Judas, Jonathan, and Simon Maccabeus had violent deaths.

42. ___ The first person killed by Mattathias as he began his revolt was a (a) royal official; (b) spy; (c) soldier; (d) Jew (1 Mc 2).

43. ___ All the following actions characterized the Maccabean revolt except: (a) refusing to fight on the Sabbath; (b) tearing down pagan altars; (c) attacking their enemies; (d) circumcising Jewish boys (1 Mc 2).

44. T F Even though Judas' army was outnumbered, he defeated forces led by Gorgias and Lysias, then rededicated the Temple at Jerusalem (1 Mc 4).

45. ___ The rededication of the Temple included all the following except: (a) choosing priests; (b) offering sacrifice on the old altar of holocausts; (c) repairing the sanctuary; (d) making new sacred vessels; (e) celebrating for eight days (1 Mc 4).

46. ___ Simon Maccabeus was killed by (a) Trypho; (b) his son-in-law, Ptolemy; (c) Syrian soldiers; (d) Cendebeus (1 Mc 16).

47. ___ Study the following statements:
1) We, like the Maccabees, are faced with the choice of accepting the principles of a secular world or those based on religious beliefs.
2) The Second Book of Maccabees describes the historical events following the years covered by 1 Maccabees.
3) The Second Book of Maccabees was meant to encourage its readers to be tolerant both of Jews who were faithful to the law and of those who accepted Hellenizing influences.

Of these statements: (a) all are true; (b) all are false; (c) 1 is false; (d) 1 and 2 are false; (e) 2 and 3 are false.

48. ___ The author's preface describes all the following except: (a) his source; (b) his desire to offer simple reading; (c) his certainty of being inspired by God; (d) his sweat and sleepless nights (2 Mc 2).

49. ___ Study the following statements:
1) In the martyrdom scene of 2 Maccabees 7, only one of the brothers expresses a belief in eternal life.
2) There is clear proof in 2 Maccabees 12 that the Jews of the second century B.C. prayed for the dead.
3) Catholic doctrines of eternal life, prayer for the dead, and the existence of purgatory find a scriptural basis in 2 Maccabees.

Of these statements: (a) 1 is true; (b) 1 and 2 are true; (c) 2 and 3 are true; (d) all are true; (e) all are false.

50. T F The Old Testament historical books show us the evil as well as the good in people and remind us of humanity's need for salvation.

CHAPTER SEVEN

The Wisdom Books

1. T F Wisdom that helps guide us through life is expressed in many forms, including drama, poetry, and proverbs.
2. T F Israel's sages learned from the Wisdom traditions of Egypt and Mesopotamia, and Israel's Wisdom Literature was basically the same as theirs.
3. T F Israel's Wisdom Literature looks at life from the viewpoint of the nation rather than that of the individual.
4. T F Authors of Old Testament Wisdom Literature discuss such topics as good manners, moral behavior, business, marriage, family, the home, social life, and human relationships.
5. T F Old Testament Wisdom Books tend to follow patterns of Jewish poetry, depending on the balance of thoughts rather than on rhyme.
6. ____ The saying "Hatred stirs up disputes, but love covers all offenses" (Prv 10:12) is an example of (a) repetition; (b) contrast; (c) construction; (d) Psalms.
7. T F The Wisdom tradition of Israel began before the time of David and continued throughout Old Testament history.
8. T F It is likely that David and Solomon were the authors of all the Wisdom Literature attributed to them.
9. T F The Book of Job was written by an inspired poet who saw the error of equating suffering with divine punishment.
10. T F Both the prose and poetry sections of the Book of Job show him as a man who patiently accepts the traditional explanations for suffering explained by his friends.

11. T F In the Book of Job, God praises Job's three friends for explaining the real reason for suffering.

12. ___ In confronting Job, God asks if Job has God's control over creation, over animals and people, and, last of all, over a beast, apparently the (a) crocodile; (b) eagle; (c) whale; (d) lion (Jb 38–41).

13. ___ The author of the Book of Job most likely found answers to the problem of pain through (a) experiencing God; (b) philosophy; (c) logic; (d) the New Testament.

14. T F The Book of Job teaches us that we ought not offer simplistic answers to life's greatest problems and that those who suffer can find peace when they realize that God is with them even in their pain.

15. T F The Book of Job is a drama, but behind it, no doubt, is a real story of anguish and suffering.

16. T F The Book of Psalms is a collection of 150 prayers in the form of Hebrew poetry.

17. ___ The founder of the Jewish psalm tradition is (a) Moses; (b) Solomon; (c) Aaron; (d) David.

18. ___ The Psalms remain popular today for all the following reasons except: (a) they give words to express our feelings; (b) they join us to the community of believers; (c) their rhyme is easily translated; (d) they are general in tone.

19. T F Because the Psalms are inspired, we should read them only for the meaning intended by the original author and ought not adapt them to our own situation.

20. T F Even though the Psalms are inspired, some of them express ideas contrary to the teaching of Jesus.

21. ___ Psalm 1 compares the one who delights in God's law to (a) David; (b) Solomon; (c) a tree; (d) incense.

22. ___ According to Psalm 90, for God, a thousand years are as (a) a moment; (b) a year; (c) forever; (d) yesterday.

23. T F Psalm 104 praises God both as Creator and as the One who sustains created things in being.

24. T F Psalm 150 counsels us to praise God with our voices but does not mention musical instruments.

25. ___ The Book of Proverbs claims as its author the "patron" of the Jewish Wisdom tradition, namely, (a) Moses; (b) Solomon; (c) Aaron; (d) David.

26. T F Much of the content of the Book of Proverbs dates after 500 B.C.

27. T F Many of the sayings in the Book of Proverbs deal with secular wisdom and mundane details of everyday life.

28. ___ According to Proverbs 1, the beginning of knowledge is (a) study; (b) fear of the Lord; (c) a wise teacher; (d) reading the Bible.

29. ___ According to Proverbs 15, what will "light up the face" is (a) money; (b) pleasure; (c) power; (d) a glad heart.

30. T F One of the most striking features of the Bible is its honesty in facing the unpleasant side of life.

31. T F Qoheleth, author of Ecclesiastes, saw little meaning in life on this earth, but he was consoled by his assurance of everlasting life.

32. T F Qoheleth, like Proverbs, teaches traditional wisdom as the answer for life's problems.

33. T F Qoheleth advised his readers to lead a moral, balanced life, without expecting too much happiness.

34. ___ The answers to the riddles of life posed by Qoheleth are ultimately found in (a) other Wisdom Literature; (b) the last chapter of Ecclesiastes; (c) Jesus Christ; (d) the Pentateuch.

35. T F Ecclesiastes 3 teaches that human beings and animals are different, because humans live after death and animals do not.

36. T F The Song of Songs may be interpreted as a love poem which can also remind us of God's love for us.

37. T F The Song of Songs was written by King Solomon.

38. ___ In Song of Songs 2, the dialogue occurs in (a) spring; (b) summer; (c) fall; (d) winter.

39. ___ In Song of Songs 8, love is said to be as (a) old as the hills; (b) beautiful as spring; (c) lasting as forever; (d) stern as death.

40. T F The Book of Wisdom was written in Greek, about the year 50, by a Jew living in Alexandria, Egypt.

41. T F Because the author of Wisdom was acquainted with Greek culture, he wanted to show the Jewish people that true wisdom could be found in Greek philosophy.

42. T F The Book of Wisdom teaches the reality of eternal life.

43. T F There is no evidence that New Testament authors were aware of the Book of Wisdom.

44. T F According to Wisdom 9, Wisdom was present when God made the world.

45. ___ In Wisdom 10:15-21, the main topic is (a) creation; (b) the Exodus; (c) sin; (d) the end of time.

46. T F Sirach was written in Hebrew and translated into Greek by the grandson of the original author.

47. ___ In some Catholic Bibles, the Book of Sirach is called the Book of (a) Wisdom; (b) Ecclesiastes; (c) Proverbs; (d) Ecclesiasticus.

48. ___ When Sirach praises God's works of creation, he includes all the following except: the (a) sun, moon, and stars; (b) rainbow, clouds, and storm; (c) snow, frost, and ice; (d) lions, oxen, and bears (Sir 42:15–43:35).

49. ___ In his praise of God the Creator, Sirach says, "Let the last word be" (a) Alleluia; (b) praise the Creator; (c) he is all in all; (d) God is good (Sir 42:15–43:35).

50. T F The Wisdom Books teach us how to build our lives on time-tested principles that flow from the inspiration of God.

CHAPTER EIGHT
The Prophetic Books

1. ___ The basic meaning of prophet in the Old Testament is one who (a) foretells the future; (b) criticizes society; (c) prays; (d) speaks for God.

2. ___ Some Old Testament prophets foretold the coming of a "Messiah," meaning (a) anointed one; (b) prophet; (c) soldier; (d) new age.

3. T F In God's plan, prophetic messages about the immediate future might foreshadow the distant future.

4. T F The only meanings which New Testament writers could correctly see in Old Testament prophecies were those actually intended by their authors.

5. ___ The prophets were primarily (a) lawyers; (b) preachers; (c) scientists; (d) theologians.

6. T F The first thirty-nine chapters of the Book of Isaiah originate from the prophet Isaiah, whose ministry was centered in Jerusalem during the years 742-701.

7. T F During Isaiah's lifetime, the Babylonian army conquered Samaria and besieged Jerusalem.

8. ___ In the Book of Isaiah, the following themes are found: (a) God's holiness; (b) the Suffering Servant; (c) new heavens and a new earth; (d) a and b; (e) a, b, and c.

9. T F When God asked for someone to speak as a representative, Isaiah, like Moses, begged God to send someone else (Is 6:1-8).

10. ___ When King Ahaz refused to believe God's promise to deliver Judah from Assyria, Isaiah gave a sign, which was a (a) sword; (b) lamb; (c) star; (d) child (Is 7:10-16).

11. ___ Study the following statements:
1) The symbolic vision of peace in Isaiah 11:1-11 includes harmony, even among animals like wolves and lambs.
2) The "Suffering Servant" songs found in Isaiah 40–55 foreshadow the salvation given to the world through the suffering and death of Jesus Christ.

Of these statements: (a) both are true; (b) both are false; (c) 1 is false, 2 is true; (d) 1 is true, 2 is false.

12. T F In the vision of the "new heavens and a new earth" found in Isaiah 65:17-25, people who live for one hundred years will be honored as old and wise.

13. T F The prophet Jeremiah was a contemporary of Isaiah and carried out his ministry before the fall of Samaria in 721.

14. T F Jeremiah was honored by the kings of Judah, especially King Jehoiakim, because he was a true prophet.

15. ___ Jeremiah's private life could be best summarized as one of (a) honor; (b) suffering; (c) triumph; (d) ease.

16. ___ Study the following statements:
1) Jeremiah was in Jerusalem when the Babylonians besieged it in 597 and when they destroyed it in 587.
2) Even when Jeremiah was scourged and placed in the stocks, he remained joyful because God had called him to be a prophet (Jer 20:1-18).
3) Jeremiah foretold that Jerusalem would be conquered and burned by Nebuchadnezzar, king of Babylon (Jer 32:26-35).
4) Through Jeremiah, God promised a covenant like the one made after the Hebrews left Egypt (Jer 31:31-34).

Of these statements: (a) 1 and 2 are false; (b) 2 and 3 are false; (c) 1 and 3 are false; (d) 2 and 4 are false; (e) all are false.

17. ___ Study the following statements:
1) The Book of Lamentations saw Jerusalem's defeat by the Babylonians as a defeat for God and, therefore, called upon God to avenge the Jews.
2) Because of the almost total destruction of Jerusalem, the author of Lamentations could not express hope for the future (Lam 2:8-13; Lam 3:17-33).

Of these statements: (a) both are false; (b) 1 is false 2 is true; (c) 1 is true, 2 is false; (d) both are true.

18. ____ The Book of Baruch was attributed to Jeremiah's secretary and was written about (a) 721; (b) 587; (c) 445; (d) 200.

19. ____ Study the following statements:

1) The Book of Baruch was written for Jews who lived far from Jerusalem but remained loyal to the idea of temple worship.

2) Baruch 5 shows that the author saw Jerusalem as a city favored by God.

Of these statements: (a) both are false; (b) 1 is false 2 is true; (c) 1 is true, 2 is false; (d) both are true.

20. ____ Ezekiel was a priest who prophesied in (a) Assyria; (b) Babylon; (c) Jerusalem; (d) Samaria.

21. T F The Book of Ezekiel uses strange language and visions to emphasize the majesty of God and the importance of liturgy and worship.

22. ____ Ezekiel's vision of God's majesty does *not* mention (a) a huge cloud; (b) four living creatures; (c) dry bones; (d) wheels; (e) wings (Ez 1).

23. T F The vision of the dry bones in Ezekiel 37:1-14 symbolizes God's promise to bring the Jews back to the land of Israel.

24. T F The Book of Daniel is a collection of fictional stories and apocalyptic messages, but it teaches the reality of everlasting life (Dn 12:1-3).

25. ____ The Book of Daniel was written to give hope to the Jews (a) in exile in Babylon; (b) as they returned from exile; (c) persecuted by Antiochus Epiphanes about 165; (d) of Alexandria, Egypt, about 100.

26. ____ Daniel was thrown into the lions' den because he (a) prayed; (b) refused to obey Nebuchadnezzar; (c) plotted against the king; (d) built a statue in honor of the true God (Dn 6).

27. ____ The vision of Daniel 12:1-3 mentions the angel (a) Gabriel; (b) Raphael; (c) Michael; (d) Daniel.

28. T F Hosea was a prophet who saw in his unfaithful wife's conduct a pattern of the way Israel treated God.

29. ___ Hosea says that God will lead Israel into the desert, where the people will learn to call God their (a) Lord; (b) king; (c) husband; (d) master (Hos 2:16-25).

30. ___ In the powerful imagery of Hosea 11, the prophet says that God loves Israel as a (a) wife; (b) child; (c) spouse; (d) nation.

31. ___ The prophecy of Joel foretold a "Day of the Lord" because of (a) Alexander the Great; (b) the Babylonians; (c) peace; (d) locusts.

32. T F Joel 3 promises that God will pour out the Spirit only upon the Israelites.

33. ___ Study the following statements:
1) Amos was a shepherd-farmer turned prophet who was sympathetic to the poor.
2) Amos came from Judah but prophesied in Israel. He was told to go home by the priest at the shrine of Bethel.
3) In Amos 5:7–6:8, the prophet tells the people to look forward to the blessings of the "Day of the Lord."
Of these statements: (a) 1 is false; (b) 2 is false; (c) 3 is false; (d) all are false; (e) all are true.

34. T F The prophet Obadiah saw the people of Edom as if they were Esau and the Israelites as if they were Jacob; he foretold ruin for the house of Esau and restoration for the house of Jacob (Ob).

35. T F Underlying the story of Jonah is the historical event of a prophet actually surviving three days in the belly of a great fish.

36. ___ The Book of Jonah is directed chiefly against the sin of (a) negligence in worship; (b) oppression of the poor; (c) selfish nationalism; (d) divorce.

37. ___ The Book of Micah is directed chiefly against the sin of (a) negligence in worship; (b) oppression of the poor; (c) selfish nationalism; (d) divorce.

38. ___ Study the following statements:
1) Micah 5:1-3 promises that a ruler who will "shepherd his flock" will come from Galilee.
2) Micah 6:1-8 proclaims that God wants people to do right, love what is good, and walk humbly with God.

Of these statements: (a) 1 is true, 2 is false; (b) both are true; (c) both are false; (d) 1 is false, 2 is true.

39. T F Nahum echoes the Jewish belief that murder and savagery must be punished by God.

40. ___ Nahum 2 portrays the king of Assyria as a (a) snake; (b) bear; (c) lion; (d) dragon.

41. T F Habakkuk was a prophet who questioned God because of the suffering he knew would befall Jerusalem. God's response could be summed up in the words "The just man, because of his faith, shall live" (Hb 1:12–2:4).

42. ___ Zephaniah was a prophet who supported the reforms begun by King (a) Josiah; (b) Manasseh; (c) Amon; (d) Hezekiah.

43. ___ In Zephaniah 3:14-20, the prophet tells the Jews to rejoice for all the following reasons except: (a) Babylon is destroyed; (b) God is in their midst; (c) God has removed judgment from them; (d) God will rejoice over them.

44. T F Haggai encouraged the Jews to rebuild the Temple with the promise that God would make its future glory greater than that of the old Temple (Hg 2:1-9).

45. ___ A prophet who, along with Haggai, urged the Jews returning from exile to rebuild the Temple was (a) Zephaniah; (b) Hezekiah; (c) Malachi; (d) Zechariah.

46. T F In Zechariah 8:1-8, the prophet has a vision of Jerusalem where all people will be eternally young.

47. T F In Zechariah 9:9-10, the prophet foretells that the savior will come to Jerusalem as a conquering king, riding on a powerful warhorse.

48. T F Malachi condemned divorce as something hateful to God and promised that God would send "Elijah the prophet" to turn the hearts of fathers to their children and the hearts of children to their fathers (Mal 2:10–3:1; 3:23-24).

49. ___ The chronological order (time order) in which these prophets appeared was (a) *Je*remiah, *Mi*cah, *E*zekiel, *Jo*el; (b) E, Je, M, Jo; (c) M, Je, E, Jo; (d) Jo, M, Je, E.

50. T F In the long run, the prophets succeeded in their mission as those who spoke for God.

CHAPTER NINE
The Gospels

1. ___ Study the following statements:
1) The territory familiar to Jesus from Mount Hermon to Jerusalem was about 120 miles long.
2) Jews lived in Galilee north of Samaria, and in Judea south of Samaria.
3) Galilee was more dry and less fertile than Samaria, and Samaria more dry and less fertile than Judea.
4) Judea was at peace during the first twelve years of Jesus' life.
Of these statements: (a) 1 and 2 are false; (b) 2 and 3 are false; (c) 3 and 4 are false; (d) all are false; (e) all are true.

2. ___ Study the following statements:
1) The wealthy Jews who collaborated with the Romans were the Sadducees.
2) The Jews who lived a community life in the desert were the Essenes.
3) The high priests and the members of the Sanhedrin were mostly Pharisees.
4) The Temple of Jesus' time was built by Herod the Great.
Of these statements: (a) all are false; (b) 1 is false; (c) 2 is false; (d) 3 is false; (e) 4 is false.

3. T F We learn of Jesus' birth from the gospels, and it is clear that these accounts of his birth deal only with natural events that fall into the category of history.

4. ___ The estimated date of Jesus' birth given in the text is (a) 14 B.C.; (b) 6 B.C.; (c) 0; (d) A.D. 6.

5. T   F   The Father of Jesus Christ is God.

6. ___   According to the gospels, Jesus, Mary, and Joseph fled to Egypt to escape Herod the Great. After his death they settled in (a) Nazareth; (b) Bethlehem; (c) Jerusalem; (d) Cana.

7. T   F   After Jesus spent 40 days fasting and praying in the desert, he was baptized by John in the Jordan and then began his public ministry.

8. ___   From the time Jesus was lost for three days while on pilgrimage to Jerusalem until he began his public ministry, there was a passage of about (a) 8 years; (b) 12 years; (c) 18 years; (d) 24 years.

9. ___   When Jesus began his public ministry, all the following officials were in power except: (a) Herod Agrippa; (b) Herod Antipas; (c) Philip; (d) Pontius Pilate; (e) Caiaphas.

10. ___   Study the following statements:

1) Jesus taught in parables and through them said that all the hopes of the human race can be realized in him.
2) An Aramaic word used by Jesus to indicate his unique authority was *Amen.*
3) Jesus spoke of God as Father, Son, and Holy Spirit and taught that we should love God with all our heart.

Of these statements: (a) all are false; (b) 1 is false; (c) 2 is false; (d) 3 is false; (e) all are true.

11. ___   Study the following statements:

1) Jesus worked miracles, astounding signs with no natural explanation.
2) Miracles occurred frequently in Jesus' ministry, but there is no evidence that they occur today.
3) Jesus apparently healed most sick people of his time.
4) Because Christ was God, he could not really be tempted.

Of these statements: (a) 1 and 2 are false; (b) 1, 2, and 3 are false; (c) 1, 3, and 4 are false; (d) 2, 3, and 4 are false; (e) all are false.

12. T F The gospels mention Jesus' power over devils, but references to them may be symbolic because the Catholic Church does not teach the existence of angels or devils.

13. ___ Jesus had special followers called apostles; each of the following groups contains names of those among the Twelve apostles except: (a) Peter, James, Andrew, and John; (b) Stephen, Paul, Joseph, and Luke; (c) Philip, Bartholomew, Judas, and Simon; (d) Judas, James, Thomas, and Matthew.

14. ___ Study the following statements:
1) In the gospels, *disciples* may refer to the twelve apostles or to a larger group of Jesus' followers.
2) Jesus' Galilean ministry is emphasized by Matthew, Mark, and Luke, but is not mentioned by John.
3) John's Gospel implies that Jesus' public ministry lasted for at least two years.

Of these statements: (a) all are false; (b) 1 is false; (c) 2 is false; (d) 3 is false; (e) all are true.

15. ___ People responded in different ways to Jesus' ministry; those most worried that Jesus might start a civil war with the Romans were the (a) Zealots; (b) Pharisees; (c) Essenes; (d) Sadducees.

16. T F Evidently, most of the crowds who followed Jesus believed that he was the Messiah and understood the kingdom of God as he taught it.

17. ___ Study the following statements:
1) Jesus would not have gone to Jerusalem if he had realized that his enemies were plotting to kill him.
2) When Jesus drove the moneychangers and the sellers from the Temple area, he enraged the Sadducees.
3) According to the gospels, on the night before he died, Jesus shared a Passover meal with his disciples.
4) The Jewish leaders wanted to stone Jesus to death, but they had to follow Jewish law and have him crucified.

Of these statements: (a) 1 and 2 are false; (b) 1 and 3 are false; (c) 1 and 4 are false; (d) 2 and 3 are false; (e) 2 and 4 are false.

18. ___ Before his execution, Jesus was seen by all the following officials except: (a) Herod the Great; (b) Pilate; (c) Herod Antipas; (d) Caiaphas.

19. T F Because Jesus was God, he could not have felt desolation or abandonment before he died.

20. ___ Study the following statements:
   1) Joseph of Arimathea, a member of the Sanhedrin, and Nicodemus, a Pharisee, buried Jesus' body.
   2) Those who first discovered that the tomb of Jesus was empty were women.
   3) According to the Gospel of John, the apostle Thomas professed his belief that Jesus is God.
   Of these statements: (a) 1 is false; (b) 2 is false; (c) 3 is false; (d) all are false; (e) all are true.

21. T F The most important sources for what we know about Jesus are the gospels, which were developed over a period of many years in a three-stage process.

22. ___ Study the following statements:
   1) The gospels are the witness not just of the four evangelists but of the Christian community.
   2) Scripture scholars today generally agree that Mark and Luke used Matthew as a source.
   3) John's Gospel developed independently of the other three, and was written by someone unfamiliar with Jewish life and customs.
   Of these statements: (a) 1 and 2 are false; (b) 2 and 3 are false; (c) 1 and 3 are false; (d) all are false; (e) all are true.

23. ___ The gospels were written primarily as (a) biographies; (b) history; (c) faith declarations; (d) scientific studies.

24. ___ The gospels and other books of the New Testament were written in (a) Hebrew; (b) Aramaic; (c) Latin; (d) Greek.

25. ___ Study the following statements:
   1) The Gospel of Matthew as we now have it was the first of the gospels to be written.
   2) Matthew's Gospel was probably written for Christians with a gentile background.
   3) The main part of Matthew's Gospel is divided into five sections, seemingly patterned on the Pentateuch.

4) The tearing of the temple veil in Matthew's Gospel is a symbol of the end of the Old Covenant.

5) A date usually given for the composition of Matthew's Gospel is around A.D. 80-85.

Of these statements: (a) 1 and 2 are false; (b) 2 and 3 are false; (c) 3 and 4 are false; (d) 3, 4, and 5 are false; (e) all are false.

26. ____ In the "Beatitudes" spoken in his Sermon on the Mount, Jesus proclaims that the "clean of heart" will (a) be comforted; (b) be children of God; (c) receive the kingdom of heaven; (d) see God (Mt 5–7).

27. ____ Study the following statements:

1) In his Sermon on the Mount, Jesus says that he has come to abolish the law and the prophets (Mt 5–7).

2) Jesus promises a heavenly reward if we love those who love us (Mt 5–7).

3) According to Jesus, no one can serve two masters (Mt 5–7).

Of these statements: (a) 1 is true; (b) 2 is true; (c) 3 is true; (d) 1 and 2 are true; (e) all are true.

28. ____ Jesus says that those will enter the kingdom of heaven who (a) call him Lord; (b) are saved; (c) know him; (d) work miracles in his name; (e) do God's will (Mt 5–7).

29. ____ Study the following statements:

1) The Gospel of Mark was the first of the four gospels to be written.

2) Mark's Gospel focuses more on the teaching of Jesus than on his active ministry.

3) The Gospel of Mark as we have it concludes with passages not written by the original author.

4) Mark's Gospel was probably written about 65-70 for gentile Christians.

Of these statements: (a) 1 is false; (b) 2 is false; (c) 3 is false; (d) 4 is false; (e) 1 and 4 are false.

30. ____ In Mark's Gospel, Jesus is recognized as Son of God by (a) Peter; (b) the crowds; (c) Pilate; (d) a centurion.

31. T F The only clear indication in the first chapter of Mark that Jesus is the Son of God is found in verse 1.

32. ____ Mark's account of the Passion does *not* mention (a) Jesus' trial before Herod; (b) Judas' betrayal of

Jesus; (c) Jesus' agony in the garden; (d) Jesus' trial before the Sanhedrin (Mk 14–15).

33. ___ Mark's account of the Passion does *not* tell about (a) two others crucified with Jesus; (b) Jesus forgiving his enemies; (c) people mocking Jesus; (d) friends of Jesus at the cross; (e) the veil in the sanctuary being torn (Mk 14–15).

34. ___ Study the following statements:
1) The Gospel of Luke was written for gentile Christians.
2) Luke saw the Old Testament as prophecy foretelling Christ, and he pointed out Jesus as Savior of all.
3) Luke's Gospel emphasizes the rejection of Jesus by the Jewish people.
Of these statements: (a) 1 is false; (b) 2 is false; (c) 3 is false; (d) 1 and 2 are false; (e) all are false.

35. ___ Study the following statements:
1) In the infancy account of Luke's Gospel, the angel who appeared to Zechariah in the Temple was Raphael.
2) The angel who appeared to Mary was Gabriel.
3) Elizabeth recognized Mary as the mother of the Lord even before Jesus was born (Lk 1-2).
Of these statements: (a) 1 is false; (b) 2 is false; (c) 3 is false; (d) 1 and 2 are false; (e) all are false.

36. ___ Luke's Gospel points out that God intends salvation for everyone. Luke's infancy account shows this in all the following ways except: (a) Caesar's decree of a census; (b) Simeon's words in the Temple; (c) the angel's announcement to the shepherds; (d) the visit of the magi (Lk 1–2).

37. T F In each of the three parables in Luke 15, there is rejoicing after something or someone lost is found.

38. ___ The Pharisees and scribes of Luke 15:2 are most likely portrayed in Luke 15:11-32 as the (a) younger brother; (b) older brother; (c) father; (d) servants.

39. ___ In Luke's account of the Resurrection (Chapter 24), Peter looked into the tomb and saw (a) an angel; (b) Jesus; (c) burial cloths; (d) nothing.

40. ___ One of those who recognized Jesus "in the breaking of the bread" was (a) Cleopas; (b) Mary Magdalene; (c) Peter; (d) Joanna (Lk 24).

41. T F The Gospel of Luke says that Jesus ascended into heaven 40 days after his Resurrection (Lk 24).

42. ___ Study the following statements:
1) Today most scholars agree that the author of the fourth gospel is John the apostle.
2) The Prologue of John's Gospel professes faith in the divinity of Jesus.
3) In describing the passion and death of Jesus, the Gospel of John emphasizes the suffering and humiliation that Christ endured for our sake.

Of these statements: (a) 1 and 2 are false; (b) 2 is false; (c) 2 and 3 are false; (d) all are false; (e) 1 and 3 are false.

43. ___ Study the following statements:
1) The sacramental life of the Church is alluded to in John's Gospel.
2) The Epilogue of John's Gospel explains that the beloved disciple would not die until Jesus came again.
3) In John's Gospel, we hear Christ speaking through the Christian community, which has been guided and directed by the Holy Spirit.

Of these statements: (a) 1 is false; (b) 2 is false; (c) 3 is false; (d) all are true; (e) all are false.

44. ___ The sixth chapter of John's Gospel illustrates how the author weaves many symbols together, in this case to point to the Eucharist. This chapter uses all these symbols except: (a) the Feast of Passover; (b) loaves and fish; (c) manna; (d) changing water to wine; (e) c and d.

45. ___ John 6 shows Jesus' power over nature, and thus his power to change bread into his body, by the miracle of (a) raising Lazarus; (b) walking on water; (c) calming the storm; (d) b, c.

46. ___ In John 6, Jesus says all the following except: (a) the bread I will give is my flesh; (b) whoever eats this bread will live forever; (c) this bread is a symbol of my body; (d) I am the bread of life.

47. T F   What Jesus was saying in John 6 was so hard to believe that many of his disciples left him.
48. ___   In John's Gospel, the first person mentioned as seeing the risen Lord is (a) Mary of Magdala; (b) Peter; (c) John; (d) the Mother of Jesus (Jn 20).
49. T F   John's Gospel relates that on Easter Sunday evening Jesus bestowed the Holy Spirit on his disciples and gave them the power to forgive sins (Jn 20).
50. T F   The last words of John 20 show that John's purpose in writing was to invite people to put faith in Christ.

CHAPTER TEN
Acts to Second Thessalonians

1. ___ All these statements are true except: (a) Christ's apostles proclaimed that he had risen from the dead, even though they were threatened with persecution and death; (b) After his Resurrection, Jesus appeared in his mortal body to his apostles and other followers; (c) According to Acts, Jesus appeared frequently to his followers, then ascended into heaven after 40 days; (d) The Ascension shows that Christ chose to make his real, spiritual presence visible through his followers; (e) Most of what we know about the Church in the years following Christ's Resurrection comes from the Acts of the Apostles.

2. ___ Study the following statements:
   1) Acts, like the Gospel of Luke, with which it forms a two-part work, is designed to show that many faithful Jews accepted Christ and that God always intended to offer salvation to all people.
   2) The Gospel of Luke shows how the gospel spread from Bethlehem to Rome; Acts shows how it spread from Rome to Jerusalem.
   3) Unlike the gospels, Acts is primarily a historical document.
   Of these statements: (a) 1 is false; (b) 1 and 2 are false; (c) 1 and 3 false; (d) 2 and 3 are false; (e) all are false.

3. ___ In Acts, Luke uses all the following techniques to convey his message except: (a) composing speeches;

(b) repetition; (c) reporting sermons word for word; (d) focusing on the ministry of Peter and Paul.

4. ___ All these statements are true except: (a) As the apostles waited for the coming of the Holy Spirit after Christ's Ascension, Mary the Mother of Jesus was with them; (b) After Peter's Pentecost sermon, about 3,000 were baptized; (c) As the Church grew, assistants called deacons were commissioned by the apostles to care for the poor; (d) Jewish authorities persecuted Christ's followers soon after Pentecost, and the first follower to be executed was Stephen; (e) Because the first Christians celebrated the breaking of the bread (the Eucharist), they did not worship in the Temple.

5. T F One who persecuted Christ's followers was Saul. He was converted and immediately began to proclaim Christ with great success in Damascus and Jerusalem.

6. ___ All these statements are true except: (a) The city where Barnabas and Saul preached to Gentiles and where Christ's followers were first called Christians was Antioch; (b) The ruler who killed James, son of Zebedee, was Herod Agrippa; (c) The young man who left Barnabas and Paul during their first missionary journey (45-48) was John Mark; (d) On their first missionary journey, Paul and Barnabas preached only to Jews; (e) When Christians met in 49 at Jerusalem to discuss the relationship between Judaism and Christianity, the crucial argument that we are saved by the grace of Christ was given by Peter.

7. ___ Study the following statements:
1) Paul's companions on his second missionary journey (50-53) included Silas and Timothy.
2) Paul was a tentmaker by trade, and while in Corinth during his second journey, he stayed with Aquila and Priscilla, who were Jews and tentmakers.
3) Paul traveled about twice as many miles on his second missionary journey as he did on his first.
Of these statements: (a) all are true; (b) 1 is false; (c) 2 is false; (d) 3 is false; (e) all are false.

8. ___ On his second journey, Paul visited all the following cities except: (a) Lystra, Troas; (b) Cyprus, Malta; (c) Philippi, Thessalonica; (d) Athens, Corinth.

9. ___ On his third missionary journey in 54-57, Paul stayed longest in (a) Ephesus; (b) Corinth; (c) Athens; (d) Troas.

10. ___ Study the following statements:

1) Acts, in relating Paul's third missionary journey, tells how Christians assembled on Sunday, the day of Christ's Resurrection.

2) Shortly after he returned from his third missionary journey, Paul visited Jerusalem, where he was welcomed by the Jewish people when he spoke at the Temple.

3) Paul, after his arrest, was taken to Caesarea to escape a plot to kill him, a plot discovered by Paul's nephew.

4) Paul was kept in prison in Caesarea for two years, first by Festus, then by Felix, who had Paul speak to Herod Agrippa II.

5) Paul was sent as a prisoner to Rome because he had appealed for a trial there.

Of these statements: (a) 1 and 2 are false; (b) 1 and 3 are false; (c) 2 and 4 are false; (d) 1, 2, and 3 are false; (e) 3, 4, and 5 are false.

11. T F After an uneventful voyage to Rome, Paul spent two years there under arrest, preaching about Christ.

12. ___ According to Acts 1-2, all these statements are true except: (a) Jesus appeared to his apostles during the 40 days after his Resurrection, then was taken up into heaven; (b) The number of those who gathered after Jesus' Ascension and chose Matthias to replace Judas was 72; (c) In his Pentecost sermon, Peter referred to the Holy Spirit, David, and Joel; (d) After Pentecost, the believers devoted themselves to the teaching of the apostles, to the communal life, to the breaking of the bread, and to prayer.

13. T F Acts 9 describes Saul's conversion: after Christ spoke to him, he went to Damascus, where Ananias prayed for him. He was baptized, then received his sight back.

14. T F Acts 14 tells how the people of Lystra almost worshiped Paul and Barnabas, then tried to kill Paul.

15. ___ In Acts 26, Paul addresses one of his hearers as some-one who believes in the prophets, namely, (a) Agrippa; (b) Festus; (c) Bernice; (d) Felix.

16. T F When Paul arrived in Rome, he was kept under guard but was allowed to speak about Christ (Acts 28:16-31).

17. T F Of the 27 books of the New Testament, 21 are letters and of these 13 are attributed to Paul.

18. ___ All these statements about Paul are true except: (a) he was born in Tarsus about A.D. 5; (b) he was an only child; (c) he was educated in Jerusalem under Gamaliel; (d) he was a Jew and a Roman citizen.

19. ___ Study the following statements:

1) Paul was executed in Rome about A.D. 63-67.

2) Romans, Paul's first letter found after Acts, was the first of his New Testament letters to be written.

3) The Christian community at Rome was especially important to Paul because it was there that he had first preached the gospel on European soil.

Of these statements: (a) 1 is false; (b) 1 and 2 are false; (c) 1 and 3 are false; (d) 1, 2, and 3 are false; (e) 2 and 3 are false.

20. ___ In Romans, Paul discusses all the following themes except: (a) all need salvation; (b) God helps us over-come any difficulty; (c) Jews are still obliged by the Mosaic Law; (d) we are the Body of Christ.

21. ___ In Romans 5:1-11, Paul says that by faith we *have* been (a) justified; (b) saved; (c) saved and justified; (d) predestined.

22. T F Paul affirms that death will not be able to separate us from the love of God (Rom 8:28-39).

23. ___ Romans 12 does not say (a) we are one body in Christ; (b) persevere in prayer; (c) conquer evil with good; (d) we have been saved by faith.

24. ___ Paul preached to the Corinthians on his second mis-sionary journey, then wrote them on his third to deal with all these problems except: (a) factions; (b) questioning the Resurrection; (c) immorality; (d) ignoring charismatic gifts.

25. T F In 1 Corinthians 1:10-25, Paul says that the believers should preserve unity because he baptized them in Christ's name.

26. ___ "As often as you eat this bread and drink the cup," you (a) partake of Christ; (b) proclaim the death of the Lord; (c) become one body; (d) live forever (1 Cor 11:26).

27. ___ The greatest of the Spirit's gifts is (a) speaking in tongues; (b) healing; (c) love; (d) faith (1 Cor 12:12–13:13).

28. ___ Paul states in 1 Corinthians 15 that the risen Christ appeared to more than (a) 100; (b) 500; (c) 1,000; (d) 3,000.

29. ___ Study the following statements:

1) Paul's Second Letter to the Corinthians may be a composite of parts of three or four letters.

2) Refuting false accusations, Paul says that he endured beatings, stoning, and shipwreck, but that he also received revelations from God (2 Cor 11:16–12:10).

Of these statements: (a) both are true; (b) both are false; (c) 1 is false; (d) 2 is false.

30. ___ Study the following statements:

1) After Paul preached in Galatia, false teachers tried to convince his converts that Jews were no longer obliged by the law of Moses.

2) When Paul sought approval for his ministry among the Gentiles, he was supported by Peter (Kephas) both in Jerusalem and in Antioch (Gal 1:11–2:21).

3) Paul explains to the Galatians that Christ has given us freedom to do whatever we want (Gal 5:13-26).

Of these statements: (a) 1 and 2 are true; (b) 2 and 3 are true; (c) 3 is true; (d) all are true; (e) all are false.

31. ___ Paul lists as the "fruit of the Spirit" all the following except: (a) hope, humility, and counsel; (b) faithfulness, gentleness, and self-control; (c) love, joy, and peace; (d) patience, kindness, and generosity (Gal 5:13-26).

32. ___ Study the following statements:

1) Most Catholic Scripture scholars agree that Ephesians was written by Paul about the year 90.

2) Ephesians teaches that the Church is the Body of Christ and is one, holy, catholic, and apostolic.

Of these statements: (a) both are true; (b) both are false; (c) 1 is true; (d) 2 is true.

33. ___ Ephesians teaches all the following except: (a) Every family in heaven and earth takes its name from the Father (Eph 3:14-21); (b) the hope that Christ may dwell in our hearts through faith (Eph 3:14-21); (c) Wives should be subordinate to husbands, not husbands to wives (Eph 5:1–6:4); (d) The love of husband and wife is related to the love of Christ for the Church (Eph 5:1–6:4); (e) The first commandment with a promise is "Honor your father and mother" (Eph 6:2).

34. ___ Study the following statements:
  1) Paul preached at Philippi on his second missionary journey and visited there on his third, but the Philippians were among his most troublesome converts.
  2) Paul wrote at least part of Philippians from prison.
  3) The Christians in Philippi had to live in a pagan, sinful environment (Phil 2:1-18).
  Of these statements: (a) all are false; (b) 1 is false; (c) 1 and 2 are false; (d) 2 and 3 are false; (e) all are true.

35. ___ In the ancient hymn quoted in Philippians 2:6-11, we find all the following lessons except: (a) Jesus, though equal with God, became one of us; (b) Jesus was obedient to death; (c) the name of Jesus is worthy of reverence; (d) the risen Christ sends the Holy Spirit on the Church.

36. ___ Paul, in Philippians 4:4-9, gives all the following advice except: (a) rejoice in the Lord; (b) be anxious to do good; (c) make your requests known to God; (d) think about what is pure and lovely.

37. ___ Each of the following statements is true except: (a) It is certain that Paul could not have been the author of Colossians; (b) The Letter to the Colossians was written primarily to oppose cultic, magical, and astrological tendencies; (c) The Gnostic heresy taught that salvation came through mystical knowledge.

38. T F Colossians teaches that we are united so closely to Christ that we can even join our sufferings to his for the sake of the Church.

39. T F Colossians 1 honors Christ as head of the body, the Church and states that the "mystery hidden from ages past" is Christ in you.

40. T F You have died, and your life is hidden with Christ in God (Col 3:1-17).

41. T F With Christians, there should be no distinctions among Jew or Greek, slave or free (Col 3:1-17).

42. ___ The "bond of perfection" is (a) faith; (b) humility; (c) hope; (d) love (Col 3:1-17).

43. ___ Each of these statements is false except: (a) Paul's First Letter to the Thessalonians is of special importance because it is almost certainly the first book of the New Testament to be written; (b) Paul, assisted by Silas and Timothy, evangelized the Thessalonians on his first missionary journey; (c) When Paul sent Timothy to visit the Thessalonians, he was disappointed to learn that they had turned from Christ to idols.

44. T F Paul teaches that at Christ's Coming those who have died and those who are alive will rise to be with the Lord always (1 Thes 4:13–5:28).

45. ___ Paul indicates that the "Day of the Lord," Christ's Second Coming, is (a) close at hand; (b) in the distant future; (c) unknown and unexpected; (d) past (1 Thes 4:13–5:28).

46. T F The Second Letter to the Thessalonians was written to help believers who were confused about the Second Coming of Christ.

47. T F A careful reading of Second Thessalonians will provide us with a timetable for the Second Coming of Christ.

48. ___ According to Second Thessalonians, those who do not work should (a) pray; (b) not eat; (c) study; (d) wait for the Lord.

49. ___ The main message of 2 Thessalonians 2 is (a) wait for God's Coming with fear and trembling; (b) avoid the lawless one; (c) do not be alarmed; (d) pay attention to the letter allegedly from Paul.

50. ___ The correct chronological order in which these books were written is (a) *M*ark, *1 T*hessalonians, *G*alatians, *L*uke; (b) M, L, 1 T, G; (c) 1 T, M, G, L; (d) 1 T, G, M, L.

CHAPTER ELEVEN

1 Timothy to Revelation

1. ___ According to the text, Peter and Paul were martyred in Rome about A.D. (a) 35; (b) 43; (c) 65; (d) 75.

2. ___ The unrest in Palestine during the late 60s had its origins in all these causes except: (a) inept Roman rulers; (b) Zealot instigation of revolt; (c) Roman confiscation of temple funds; (d) the call by Sadducees for new government.

3. ___ All these statements are true except: (a) By the time Peter and Paul died, Christianity had spread to Asia Minor, Europe, and Africa; (b) Jewish rebellion against Rome began in Jerusalem, and spread quickly throughout Palestine; (c) The Roman general Vespasian placed his son Titus in charge of the siege of Jerusalem because Vespasian became ill; (d) Jerusalem was besieged by an army of 80 thousand led by Titus, and fell to the Romans in 70.

4. ___ Study the following statements:
1) A final Jewish rebellion began in 131 when a temple to Jupiter was planned for Jerusalem by Emperor Hadrian.
2) Because of the skillful leadership of the Jewish guerrilla fighter, Simon bar Kokhba, the Romans could never gain control of Palestine and Jerusalem.
3) Most Christians in Jerusalem when the Jewish rebellion began in 66 suffered the same fate as the Jews.
Of these statements: (a) 1 and 2 are false; (b) 2 and 3 are false; (c) 1 and 3 are false; (d) all are false; (e) all are true.

5. ___ Study the following statements:
   1) The spread of Christianity was facilitated by Roman roads and Roman policing of sea lanes.
   2) The usual places of worship for first-century Christians were churches modeled after Jewish synagogues.
   3) By the end of the first century, Christians numbered about 300,000-500,000.
   4) After Jerusalem's destruction, Christian leadership centered in Antioch, Ephesus, and Alexandria, and Rome had no special prominence until the fourth century.

   Of these statements: (a) all are true; (b) all are false; (c) 1 and 2 are false; (d) 3 and 4 are false; (e) 2 and 4 are false.

6. ___ Study the following statements:
   1) Because Christians refused to take part in the Roman state religion, they were often perceived as disloyal.
   2) The first Roman emperor to launch a general persecution against Christians was Domitian.
   3) The number of Christians martyred in Roman persecutions probably ran into the tens of thousands.
   4) In 313 the Emperor Constantine issued the decree of Milan, granting religious tolerance to Christians.

   Of these statements: (a) all are true; (b) all are false; (c) 1 and 2 are false; (d) 2 and 3 are false; (e) 3 and 4 are false.

7. ___ Most New Testament books were written, at the earliest, by the year (a) 40; (b) 100; (c) 313; (d) 400.

8. ___ Titus and 1 and 2 Timothy are letters classified as (a) catholic; (b) apocryphal; (c) pastoral; (d) wisdom.

9. ___ Each of these statements is false except: (a) Titus and 1 and 2 Timothy can be recognized as inspired by God only if actually written by Paul; (b) 1 Timothy presents Paul as writing to Timothy, whom Paul had set over the church at Tarsus; (c) Paul warned Timothy against false teachers who asserted that the body was good and the spirit evil; (d) We can see the development of organization in the early Church in 1 Timothy, which mentions bishops, presbyters, and deacons.

10. T F 1 Timothy 1 refers to Paul as an apostle but also as a sinner, and 2 Timothy presents Paul as writing Timothy from prison.

11. ___ 1 Timothy 3 states that bishops must be all the following except: (a) hospitable; (b) unmarried; (c) able to teach; (d) able managers.

12. T F According to 2 Timothy 1, Timothy's mother, Eunice, and grandmother, Lois, were both Christians.

13. ___ In teaching Timothy to pass on the faith, Paul uses all these examples except: (a) a soldier; (b) a farmer; (c) a potter; (d) an athlete (2 Tm 1–2).

14. ___ Study the following statements:
1) Titus, to whom the New Testament letter is addressed, was Paul's associate who served in Greece, Dalmatia, and Crete.
2) While Paul and the twelve apostles were alive, only they appointed presbyters and bishops.
3) By the time the Letter to Titus was written, the question of whether Christians had to observe the Mosaic Law was no longer an issue.
4) Because of persecutions, Paul had to advise Titus not to obey the civil rulers on Crete (Titus 2:11–3:7).
Of these statements: (a) 1 is true; (b) 1 and 2 true; (c) 2 and 3 are true; (d) 3 and 4 are true; (e) all are false.

15. ___ The Letter to Philemon is a personal request from Paul on behalf of a slave named (a) Apphia; (b) Archippus; (c) Philemon; (d) Onesimus.

16. ___ Study the following statements:
1) The Letter to the Hebrews is actually a sermon.
2) The Letter to the Hebrews was originally written in Hebrew.
3) The content of Hebrews indicates that it was intended for new converts.
4) Hebrews speaks of Christ's priesthood as being like that of Aaron.
Of these statements: (a) all are true; (b) all are false; (c) 1 and 2 are false; (d) 1 and 3 are false; (e) 2, 3, and 4 are false.

17. T F Hebrews invites us to see great leaders of the Old Testament as models of faith.

18. ___ Hebrews compares God's word to (a) light; (b) a sword; (c) the sun; (d) gold (Heb 4:1–5:10).

19. ___ Each of these statements is false except: (a) Christ was tested like us in every way, yet without sin (Heb 4:1–

5:10); (b) Hebrews assures us that in all his sufferings, Christ was so courageous that he never cried (Heb 4:1–5:10); (c) Hebrews 10:19-39 teaches that those who have put their faith in Christ cannot lose their salvation.

20. T F Some of those to whom Hebrews was addressed had suffered imprisonment and confiscation of property (Heb 10:19-39).

21. ___ Hebrews 12:18-24 speaks of heaven in all these symbolic terms except: (a) heavenly Jerusalem; (b) Mount Zion; (c) city of the living God; (d) eternal rest.

22. T F The Letter of James is Jewish in style but was written in excellent Greek.

23. T F James teaches that faith without good works is dead (Jas 2:14–3:12).

24. T F James says that those who are sick should be anointed with oil; the prayer of faith will save them, the Lord will raise them up, and their sins will be forgiven (Jas 5:13-16).

25. ___ In 1 Peter, there are many references to the sacrament of (a) Matrimony; (b) Eucharist; (c) Penance; (d) Anointing of the Sick; (e) Baptism.

26. T F Some scholars think that 1 Peter was written by a later author and attributed to Peter, but it certainly points to the special place of Peter in the early Church.

27. ___ Study the following statements:

1) Successors of Peter as Bishop of Rome were eventually seen to have a special place among bishops, just as Peter had a special place among the apostles.

2) According to 1 Peter, we have been redeemed by the blood of Christ (1 Pt 1:1–2:10).

3) 1 Peter addresses the baptized as a chosen race, a royal priesthood, a holy nation, and a people of God's own (1 Pt 1:1–2:10).

Of these statements: (a) 1 is false; (b) 2 is false; (c) 3 is false; (d) all are true; (e) all are false.

28. ___ Peter counsels us to put our trust in God and to be always vigilant because the devil is like a (a) dragon; (b) bear; (c) lion; (d) criminal (1 Pt 5:6-11).

29. T F There is some question about the authorship of both 1 Peter and 2 Peter, but it is more likely that 2 Peter actually came from Peter the apostle.

30. T F The main point of 2 Peter is that God's judgment will certainly come, even though the exact time is unknown.

31. ___ All these statements are true except: (a) Scholars generally agree that the three letters of John were written by John the apostle; (b) 1 John emphasizes belief in the humanity of Jesus Christ and in the reality of Christ's divine sonship; (c) The author of 1 John had to deal with false teachers who said that Jesus was not really Son of God and that Jesus was not truly human.

32. T F In mentioning the fact of Christ's becoming human, 1 John 1:1-4 mentions the senses of sight, hearing, and touch.

33. T F The main point of 1 John 4:7-21 is that when we live good lives and show our love for God, God begins to love us and offer us eternal life.

34. T F 1 John 4:7-21 teaches clearly that Jesus is the Son of God.

35. T F There is apparently no real connection between 1 John and 2 John.

36. T F The Second Book of John encourages Christians to welcome false teachers in order to try to convert them.

37. ___ The Third Book of John is concerned with missionary activity in the early Church and with problems of authority. The person who refused to accept the "presbyter's" authority was (a) Gaius; (b) Diotrephes; (c) Demetrius; (d) unnamed.

38. ___ The Letter of Jude attacks false teachers who promote license instead of liberty. He attacks them by calling them all the following except: (a) waterless springs; (b) fruitless trees; (c) waterless clouds; (d) wandering stars.

39. ___ Jude makes several references to the Old Testament and mentions all the following except: (a) the Exodus from Egypt; (b) Sodom and Gomorrah; (c) Cain; (d) Abraham.

40. ___ Apocalyptic literature originated during times of persecution and was intended to encourage readers in their trials. An Old Testament example is the Book of (a) Wisdom; (b) Genesis; (c) Daniel; (d) Jonah.

41. ___ Apocalyptic literature assigned special meanings to numbers. The number which signified perfection was (a) 4; (b) 7; (c) 12; (d) 1000.

42. ___ Study the following statements:
1) The main purpose of apocalyptic literature was to foretell the future, especially details of the end of the world.
2) The Book of Revelation is an epic presentation of the battle between good and evil, and an inspired promise that good will triumph.
3) Revelation teaches that Jesus is God.
4) Revelation mentions God the Father and Jesus as Son of God but does not mention the Holy Spirit.

Of these statements: (a) all are true; (b) all are false; (c) 1 and 2 are false; (d) 2 and 3 are false; (e) 1 and 4 are false.

43. T F The Book of Revelation states that it was written by John the Apostle while he was in exile on the island of Patmos.

44. ___ In Revelation, "Babylon the Great" refers to (a) ancient Babylon; (b) Egypt; (c) Rome; (d) hell.

45. ___ While on the island of Patmos, on the Lord's Day, John had a vision in which he saw (a) an angel; (b) Satan; (c) four horsemen; (d) Christ (Rv 1).

46. T F In his letter to the church at Ephesus, John praises members of the community because they have held fast to their first love (Rv 1:1–2:7).

47. T F In the vision of the woman and the dragon, the dragon is defeated by Michael and is no longer able to attack the woman's offspring (Rv 12).

48. T F In the new heaven and a new earth, God will wipe away all tears from the eyes of God's people (Rv 21:1-8).

49. T F The Book of Revelation acknowledges all the struggles people have undergone because of sin, but it also lets us know that God's love and Christ's salvation are the greatest powers in the universe.

50. T F Revelation and the entire Bible invite us to put our trust in the word of God and accept God's kingdom offered us through Jesus Christ.

CHAPTER TWELVE

The Bible: A Book for Life

1. T F Before the time of Christ, God spoke only to the Jews, because they were the Chosen People.
2. T F Evil has come into the world because people have misused the gift of freedom given them by God.
3. T F Without freedom, no one could choose evil, but without freedom, no one could choose good, or love, or enjoy the unity of heart with others and with God that is the greatest possible human endeavor.
4. T F One pure act of love outweighs all the evil in the universe.
5. T F It is possible for human beings to take in and comprehend all the wisdom and power of God.
6. T F The Bible teaches that God exists, but it does not teach that God is Father, Son, and Holy Spirit.
7. T F The Bible teaches that union with God is the purpose and goal of human life.
8. T F God made evil as well as good so that human beings might grow stronger by learning to endure trials and sufferings.
9. T F When people say no to God, they sin.
10. T F God's love has reached out to us in the beauty of nature, in every blessing that has ever touched a human being, in moments of prayer and worship, in the teaching of spiritual leaders, and in the good lives of those who have followed God's way.
11. T F Because Jesus entered into our world, believers can be sure that they will not have to endure evil and suffering.

12. T F We can find happiness and peace by accepting Jesus Christ, living according to his guidelines, recognizing his presence in the Church, and becoming a part of that presence.

13. T F It is possible to find complete fulfillment and perfect happiness in this world.

14. T F For the believer, death can be birth to everlasting life.

15. T F The answers to all of life's problems and questions are found in the Bible.

16. T F Catholics believe that God has revealed truths to the Church which are not found explicitly in the Bible.

17. T F The Bible teaches us that God's word may be found both in the Bible and in sacred tradition.

18. T F Because we should believe only what we find in the Bible, there could have been no time when the Church did not have the New Testament.

19. T F Sacred tradition had to be a reality, or there would have been no way to determine which books belonged in the Bible and which did not.

20. T F Most of the basic dogmas of the Catholic faith can be found explicitly in the Bible, and all Catholic beliefs are in harmony with the Bible.

21. T F Catholics depend both on the Bible and on tradition as sources of the truths they believe, and they do this on the authority of the Bible itself.

22. T F Tradition helps Catholics understand and interpret the Bible, including expressions like the "brothers and sisters" of Jesus.

23. T F In both the Old and New Testaments, "brothers and sisters" might refer to people who were not children of the same parents.

24. T F The New Testament refers to brothers and sisters of Jesus and to other children of Mary and Joseph.

25. T F The Catholic Church teaches that Jesus had no blood brothers and sisters, but there is no evidence that this was a belief of the Church before the time of Saint Jerome.

26. T F The Church's belief in the perpetual virginity of Mary points to the uniqueness of Jesus as the only Son of God and as our Savior.

27. T F   Since we are the Body of Christ, Mary is our mother, and she has the same mother's love for us that she has for Jesus.

28. T F   Tradition helps Catholics to apply the teachings of the Bible to modern problems, such as abortion.

29. T F   Catholics and many other Christians believe that the commandment "You shall not kill" forbids the killing of unborn children.

30. T F   The official teachers of the Catholic Church consult the Bible, sacred tradition, and the findings of modern medical science in forming the Catholic stance against abortion.

31. T F   Both the Bible and tradition are the word of God, and both can guide us to eternal life.

32. T F   The text recommends that further study should begin with the reading of the Old Testament.

33. T F   There is a special value in studying the Bible with others.

34. T F   Those who attend Mass will hear readings from the Bible each time they participate.

35. T F   When we pick up the Bible, we dial God's number. And God is always eager to answer.

NOTES